Rugrats'
Favorite
Funnies

ISBN 0-439-46349-1

12 11 10 9 8 7 6 5 4 3 2 1   3 4 5 6 7 8/0

Printed in the U.S.A.

First Scholastic printing, September 2003

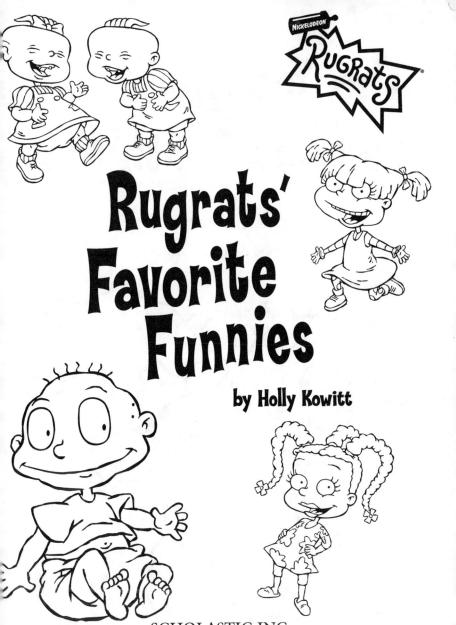

Rugrats' Favorite Funnies

by Holly Kowitt

SCHOLASTIC INC.

New York Toronto London Auckland Sydney
Mexico City New Delhi Hong Kong Buenos Aires

The Young and the Toothless

What does the babies' telephone have?

Crawler I.D.

How do you get
an astronaut baby
to sleep?

You rocket.

Knock-knock.

Who's there?

Baby Scott.

Baby Scott who?

Baby's gotta do
what a baby's
gotta do!

How do babies swim?

They do the crawl.

What do you call babies who write to each other?

Play-pen pals.

Why did the crying baby leave his answering machine on?

He wanted to scream his calls.

What is a crying baby's favorite sport?

Bawling.

Hold the Pickles

Where does Tommy's brother like to eat?

A Dil-licatessen.

What does Tommy's brother think about milk?

It's Dil-licious!

What did the bug say when Tommy swallowed it?

Now I'm really in a Pickle!

What did Tommy say to Dil?

"I challenge you to a drool."

What types of jokes does Tommy tell?

Block-block jokes.

How is Tommy like ink?

They both run out of a pen.

Why is Spike hot in the summer?

Because he wears a coat and pants.

Bone to Be Wild

Why did Spike jump on his food?

It was lunge time.

What do Lil
and Phil
make Spike
for dessert?

Mutt pies.

How did Spike stop the Reptar movie?

He hit the paws button.

Buggin' Out!

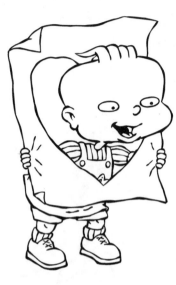

What did Phil give Lil
for Valentine's Day?

Bugs and kisses!

What did the babies give
everyone at the mud party?

A worm welcome.

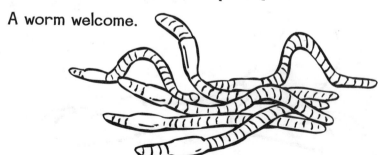

Why did Betty and Howard enter their kids in the Playground Olympics?

They wanted them twin.

Why are Phil and Lil so happy?

They eat whatever bugs them.

Why didn't Phil
go to the
earthworm
party?

He wasn't in
the mud.

Why does Lil
make a good
cupid?

She already
has a bow.

Who carries a basket and eats lint?

Lil Red Riding Hood

What did Phil say when a worm crawled on him?

Mmm, lunch is on me!

Chuckie Chuckles

What's Chuckie's favorite game?

Sneeze-tag.

How is Chuckie's nose like a track star?

They both run!

How is Chuckie like an elevator?

They're both coming down with something.

If Chuckie were a toad, what would he be covered with?

Worrywarts.

Tommy: Hey, Chuckie, what do you hate to hear at bedtime?

Chuckie: Scary tales!

Why do Chuckie and Tommy play in the garden?

They're best buds.

What dessert is Chuckie afraid of?

Troll House cookies.

Why did Angelica toss the baby toilet at Chuckie?

She wanted to throw him a surprise potty.

What's the Poop?

What vegetables do you find in diapers?

Leeks.

Why did the diapered baby leave the restaurant?

No one would take his odor!

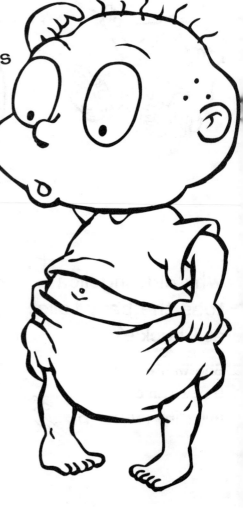

What happened when the diaper wrote a book?

It became a best-smeller.

What do diapered babies play?

Follow-the-leaker.

Angelica's Antics

What does Angelica have under her shirt?

A bully button.

If Angelica were an animal, what would she be?

A cheetah.

Why does Angelica like Thanksgiving?

It's a time to give pranks.

Where do babies who are babysat by Angelica end up?

In the bossed-and-found.

Why was Angelica a bee for Halloween?

She likes to buzz people around.

What did
Angelica say
when she
was waiting
for her
photos?

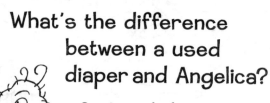

Someday
my prints
will come.

Why did Angelica
leave the dressmaker?

She was tired of being
around dummies.

What's the difference
between a used
diaper and Angelica?

One's soiled,
one's spoiled.

Why does the doctor put Angelica on the scale?

She always gets her weigh.

Why does Angelica want to go to beauty school?

So she can tease hair.

On a Pickles family car trip where can babies who annoy Angelica get out?

The pest stops.

Susie Smiles

How is Susie like
a firefly?

She's very
bright!

Why did
Susie wear
round ears for
Halloween?

'Cause she's
mice to everyone.

How is Susie like the Big Dipper?

Everyone looks up to her.

Why did Susie rise to meet the children's book author?

She stands up for what is write.

Susie: How do
babies
travel for free?

Angelica: With frequent
crier miles.

Angelica: Why
did the bald
baby want a
pet rabbit?

Susie: He needed
the hare.

What did Susie say to the noisy vegetables when she was reading?

Quiet, peas!

Kimi Kracks Up

Why does Chuckie like to protect his little sister, Kimi?

Because she never looks before she leaks.

How does Kimi describe an imaginary tree?

She's good at make be-leaf.

Where would Kimi like to live?

Imagi-nation.

Why can't Kimi ride the bus?

She's fare-less.

Takes One to Gnaw One

Why did Reptar
  eat the tightrope
  walker?

He wanted a
balanced meal.

What do you
  get when Reptar
  walks through
  your garden?

Squash.

What time is it
when the highway
is jammed with
Reptars?

Crush hour.

What kind of
music does
everyone's
favorite
dinosaur
like?

Rap-tar music.

What does Reptar give buildings?

His stomp of approval.

What do you call Reptar
when he complains?

A whino-saur.

What do you get
when you cross
Reptar and
Grandpa
Lou?

Dino-snores.

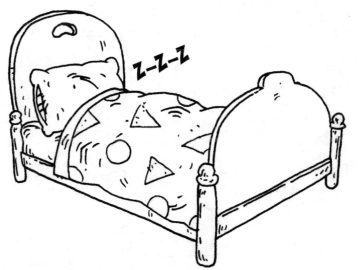

Rhyme Time

What do you call?...

a baby snake's underwear?

A viper diaper.

a crazy snack?

A kooky cookie.

a kiss from
Spike?

A pooch
smooch.

a buggy for a
cold climate?

A polar stroller.

What do you call?...

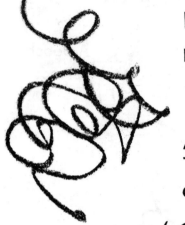

Fifi's scribbles?

Poodle doodles.

A member of
Tommy's family who
changes his mind?

A fickle Pickle.

a bathroom
heartthrob?

A potty hottie.

a sheep
named
Angelica?

A woolly bully.

Pleased to Eat You

Why did the cookie go to the doctor?

It was feeling crummy.

Why did Didi put Tommy's food in the blender?

She wanted whirled peas.

How did Stu find out that Grandpa Lou had false teeth?

They came out in conversation.

Why does Tommy want a pet bird?

He loves tweets!

Baby Babbles

What
do baby
strawberries
wear to sleep?

Their jammies.

Why did the baby
tire cry?

It needed to
be changed.

What do baby ghosts play?

Peekaboo!

What do you do to baby
boats at night?

Tug them in bed.

Why did the baby
snake cry?

It lost its rattle.

Mess O' Knock-Knocks

Knock-knock.
Who's there?
Ooze.
Ooze who?
Ooze going to change my diaper?

Knock-knock.
Who's there?
Pasture.
Pasture who?
Pasture bedtime, isn't it?

Knock-knock.
Who's there?
Boo.
Boo who?
Stop crying and open the door!